ONE *(half)* DAY AT A TIME

Doreen Rawlins

One *(half)* Day at a Time

For Jerry

Together we've climbed mountains;
Together we will walk this valley.

INTRODUCTION

First, I am not a doctor, or a psychologist, or an expert on the topic of dementia. While writing this, I've come to realize I'm not even a very good caregiver. But I try hard to practice what I preach in the caregiving of my husband. We've been married over six decades. He's worked hard most of those years to provide a wonderful life for me. I could do nothing less, then care for him in his declining mental health. It's been at least ten years since early signs of dementia began to show themselves. Today, I would categorize him as an eighty-three-year-old man, suffering late stage dementia.

There are many books and articles these days about Alzheimer Care, focusing primarily on the patient. Sometimes they include a chapter on taking care of yourself; the caregiver. You know, things like eat right, get plenty of sleep (really?) and exercise. Now and then, they suggest you hire respite care, so you can go out with the girls.

Some books on caregiving, the author asserts to being full time caregiver, but then says they 'leave to go home'. Or maybe they arrive in the morning after breakfast and spend a few hours visiting. Or that they take their husband, or wife or parent, to an appointment or for an outing of some kind, maybe to lunch.

This book addresses the full-time, 'round the clock, twenty-four/seven caregiver. The one who feels like she's swimming in the ocean at times; deep and endless, threatening to pull her under. Honey, if this is you, my prayer is that you will be inspired to change your perspective, that your energy and courage will be bolstered and your shaky faith deepened. You are not alone on this journey.

You will find fifty-two sections in this little volume, one for each week of the year, including helpful suggestions, encouraging quotes and blank pages for your own words.

So, as Dory would say "just keep swimming, just keep swimming" – one half day at a time.

The premise of this book is about changing the way you think about things. *You*, dear caregiver, must change your perspective. Make peace with the facts. Your traveling days are probably over. Your entertaining days are over. Your socializing is minimal. Your yoga class, your lunches out, your poking around in antique shops, most likely over. Much of the time, you are a homebody, stuck in so many square feet with a stranger. One minute he's happy and thinks you are beautiful, the next he's paranoid about a phone call. You can't win. It's tempting to argue, but number one rule, don't. Speak as few words as possible and agree as much as you can. When he says, he was in the NBA, played tennis with Andy Murray, was there when David killed Goliath, just say, "Oh, that's nice."

People suffering dementia are like snowflakes, no two exactly alike. The symptoms are all over the map. But the principle is the same. Caregivers have accepted the responsibility to care for that person for one reason or another. The symptoms of the patient and the reasoning behind your decision to care for him really don't matter. In fact, the perspective we caregivers strive for can adapt to any life situation. In simple terms, it's learning to make lemonade – when life hands us lemons.

The wife of a famous evangelist, Billy Sunday set her own wishes aside to travel with and support her husband. She was quoted as saying, "My job is Billy."

My job is _____. (fill in the blank)

"If you don't like something, change it. If you can't change it, change the way you think about it." Mary Englebreit

One (half) Day At A Time

I get up early, before my husband and settle myself with coffee and several inspirational books, a Bible and a journal. This is prime time for me. It will take getting used to, sitting still, praying and writing in your journal. If you can't think of anything to write, try listing things you're thankful for. You will find that life's little pleasures become more meaningful; good books, hot coffee, music and a good basketball game. Those are some of mine, along with the people in my family and friends. I've been doing this ritual for years and it truly anchors me for the day. It's my first "Pleasant Inn" along the way, to quote CS Lewis, when referring to life's hard journey. It's part of the transformation into your new way of thinking.

In a recent comic strip, "Rat" wrote a book entitled, "How to Appreciate All that is Around You." The contents: *Lower your expectations immensely*. I think he's onto something. Perhaps at one time, you traveled the world, maybe spending hours researching the details; flights, hotels, tourist attractions. That was then; this is now. Instead of mourning the past, fill the present with new things; lower your expectations. Our neighbors are excited, planning a month-long trip to some exotic place. Me? I can't wait to see the UPS man pull up. He'll be delivering my new book from Amazon. It's all relative.

"The secret of happiness is not to do what you like to do, but to learn to like what you <u>have</u> to do." King George V

_____

_____

_____

_____

_____

_____

_____

_____

_____

_____

_____

_____

_____

_____

This is not my first rodeo. Before my husband's decline, we took care of his mother, who suffered from the same thing. It had been important to her (when she was in her right mind) to look good; hair, make-up, her clothing coordinated. She was a darling little lady. It was my goal to keep her that way. During the time she lived in our home, I made sure she was bathed every day, her hair and make-up done just right, and her outfit fresh and stylish.

Although he's not as cooperative, I do the same for my husband. Whatever it takes to keep him looking good, smelling good and dressed appropriately. Hygiene is often the first to go. Left to himself, he would never take a shower, brush his teeth and sometimes, wear yesterday's clothes on top of his pajamas. It's a battle, getting him into the shower. He gets angry and refuses, no matter my coercions. Eventually, helping him undress, he'll reluctantly get in. I've had to lower my standards to a shower less often, just to cut down on stress for both of us. Our outings are planned accordingly.

Every day I try to put myself in his shoes. I try to imagine how I would feel. I hope someone would take care of me; make sure I smelled fresh and looked nice. Even if I didn't know the difference. It's the caregiver's Golden Rule. How would *you* want to be cared for?

"In everything, do to others what you would have them do to you." Matthew 7:12 *

---

* LB

_____

_____

_____

_____

_____

_____

_____

_____

_____

_____

_____

_____

_____

_____

Each morning during my quiet time, I pray for, among other things: *patience*. (And I want it NOW!) But sometimes, I confess to losing it. After so many decades of living with a person, even when you know he doesn't understand, you expect certain responses. Some things are just logical. Right? But he is not that person anymore. He simply doesn't "get it". He will only continue to fail; to understand less, to communicate less. So, dear one, *we caregivers* must change. *We*, the sleep-deprived, over-wrought, nervous-wreck, carpet-spotting, toilet-cleaning, endless laundry doing – caregiver, must be the one to change our thinking.

A few days ago, he climbed in bed with his shoes on. I had just changed the sheets. My response wasn't kind and sweet. I reacted without thinking. "What's wrong with you? Do you know where those shoes have been?" On and on I went. He gets defensive in those situations usually advising me, *this is my house and I'll do what I want!* Which makes me even more angry. These outbursts tend to filter through the rest of the day, mostly because I'm mad at myself. I go to bed feeling the burden of failure. He, on the other hand – remembers nothing. I guess in a way, that's the beauty of it.

"Anger: By sounding off, you run the risk of making the finest speech you'll ever regret!" Mike Silva

One (half) Day At A Time

_____

_____

_____

_____

_____

_____

_____

_____

_____

_____

_____

_____

_____

_____

_____

It's a dirty job, but somebody has to do it. Right? As time goes by, you will find yourself looking for "solutions." We went through a phase of clogged toilets; having to call a plumber at times. Often it was some foreign object, a shredded-up newspaper, a plastic cup, a pair of underwear. Those are problems you must always be on the alert for. As for everyday use, I did two things that made a difference. Shopped for and found single-ply toilet paper and invested in a commercial type plunger. My ear is tuned-in to the sound of flushing every time he heads in that direction.

You may be or not, dealing with incontinence. Don't let it scare you. Just be prepared. I have purchased protective pads for the bed, as well as Depends for Men, even though we're not there yet. By the way, these things can be purchased on Amazon. What I'm facing now in that area, is confusion and carelessness. Consequently, each morning I find surprises to clean up, a trail of urine spots from the bed to the bathroom and on a few occasions a complete slipup, where he mistook a drawer in the bedroom for the toilet!

This has rarely happened, but I'm always on the lookout. For spotting carpet, I use a "Spot Shot".

Our bed linens and comforters are white because I use a bathroom cleaner with bleach, for instantly cleaning up smudges. It's a bit strong, so best to open the window a crack, spray on just a smidgen, and rub out the stain with a white terry rag. Then, go ahead and make the bed. It will dry quickly and leave a fresh smell. The product is "Clorox Bathroom Cleaner" with bleach. Just be sure to keep it out of reach, just as you would for a child or invest in safety locks. Don't use this bathroom cleaner on colored fabric or carpeting. It will bleach out the color. So, make peace with your rubber gloves sweetie, and roll up your sleeves.

"The highest vocation we can have is to love. Love in action is service." Ken Essien

It started several year ago, his wandering during the night, mostly looking for cookies. He would go from cupboard to cupboard in the kitchen, pulling out boxes of cornmeal, cake mix, cereal – whatever he could get his hands on and rip it open looking for cookies. After months of cleaning up the messes, losing sleep and getting frustrated, I came up with a solution. (remember, think "solutions") I started leaving two or three Golden Oreos in a baggie, on the kitchen counter near a night light. (By the way, night-lights in the kitchen, bathroom and hallway, are essential.) He's been perfectly happy finding a little bag of cookies and never again bothered with getting into the cupboards. He takes the cookies and leaves the baggie, so the next time he gets up, when seeing an empty baggie, he must assume the cookies are all gone. It's a nightly ritual, and you may be thinking I'm contributing to too much sugar. At this stage, my strategy is to keep him content.

We each have our own bed these days, but I tend to sleep with one eye open. (it's a woman thing) Early on, whenever he would wander during the night, I would jump up and try to convince him to get back in bed. Then, of course I would be wide awake, sometimes for the rest of the night. And you know how that is. You lay there worrying about things that seem huge at night. I was losing lots of sleep. Over time though it's gotten better. If his cookies are on the kitchen counter and all sharp objects put away, I just stay quiet and let him wander. Sometimes he'll get fully dressed at two or three in the morning! Eventually he'll climb back in bed – usually with his clothes on. I just let it go, keep myself quiet and usually can go back to sleep.

"The best bridge between despair and hope is a good night's sleep." E. Joseph Cossman

A biggie is the issue of driving. It would never have worked to take the keys away from him. He is not the type to willingly give up driving. You will know when it's time to do something about it. Don't wait until there's an accident.

It's been nearly four years ago, that I noticed more and more scratches and scrapes on every corner of our white Jeep. His perception was going. He started believing the word STOP on a big red sign, did not apply to him. He never knew which way to turn and cut other cars off on roundabouts.

To get him off the roads, I knew it would have to come from someone with authority. I made an appointment with our doctor for *me*, to discuss a strategy. She would make it happen. My job was getting him there. Not an easy assignment because he's always been anti-going to the doctor! By the grace of God, a bursitis the size of a tennis ball developed on his elbow. Still it took some convincing, but I got him into her office. After checking his bursitis (which eventually went away by itself) she gave him a simple memory test. He missed fifteen of thirty questions, enough to send an order to DMV. She told him in no uncertain terms, from that moment on, he could no longer drive. To my amazement, he followed orders. Every now and then, he claims he's getting his driver's license back. I just say, "Oh well. I don't mind driving honey. Let's go get some ice cream."

You must come up with your own strategy, but the sooner you address this issue, the better – for obvious reasons. It's because you love him.

"Life comes from physical survival, but the good life comes from what we care about and how we invest our love." Rollo May

_____

_____

_____

_____

_____

_____

_____

_____

_____

_____

_____

_____

_____

_____

_____

_____

Simplify, simplify, simplify! It won't happen overnight, but begin somewhere, to eliminate excess and to scale down. Four years ago, we moved into a retirement community. If you're considering a move like that sometime in the future, I encourage you to get the ball rolling sooner rather than later. We live in a lovely, little place with floor to ceiling windows and a wonderful view. Our monthly payment includes, utilities, housekeeping, maintenance and delicious meals in a formal dining room. After living in a grand house with six bathrooms, I was reluctant to move into a one bedroom, one bath. But for our circumstances it's turned out perfect. I love it. Sure, we had to get rid of lots of stuff but I haven't missed a thing. I hear it from my neighbors all the time and must agree. 'Wish we'd have done it sooner!'

Perhaps it's become necessary for you – on top of everything else – to take over the banking. Early on, he welcomed my help, as long as he was still in charge. Gradually he did less, and I did more. It was quite honestly a big mess when I took it over completely. We had ten accounts in each of two banks, numerous lines of credit and tangled, jumbled records. It's taken a few years, but we now have two accounts at one bank and all credit lines paid off. I have a banker that is very helpful, and I've learned to prepare tax information on Quicken for our CPA.

Just recently, I met with an Estate Planning Attorney, to get our affairs in order. Each step is time consuming and complex because I'm doing it all with my sweet "ball and chain" in tow. Each of these steps have led to a much simpler life, resulting in a more cool, calm and collected caregiver.

"Courage is doing what you are afraid to do. There can be no courage unless you're scared." *Eddie Rickenbacker*

Earlier I encouraged you, instead of mourning the past, fill your life with new things! What *new thing* can you do while simultaneously caregiving? My husband is happiest when he can see me. His chair is strategically placed so he can see out the window to the right, the TV straight ahead and me in an open kitchen, to the left. Off and on during the day, and after dinner in the evening, I sit near him and work on my computer or we watch TV together. He's most content then, when I'm sitting close by. I'm not sure how it evolved, but sitting there in the evenings, I began to write fiction. My love for it grew. I found myself thinking about plots and characters throughout the day. I would type away in the evening and clean it up in the morning after my devotions. (while he was still in bed.) Somehow it developed into my first book which led to the self-publishing process. My book is on Amazon and I've just completed the manuscript for a sequel. It's like therapy for me. Writing lifts my spirits; gives me a sense of hope.

Perhaps you used to be into art or music. Pick it up again. Maybe you love to cook or knit or create scrapbooks. Have you tried coloring?

If you're familiar with working on a computer, try writing stories from childhood memories. Or doing research about your ancestors. Or research something else that grabs your interest. The computer is truly a great thing. If you're not tech savvy, have one of your kids or grandkids help you with the basics. Email conversations with friends and family are a highlight for me and shopping online is the only way to go!

Recently, I thought of a new idea and invested twenty bucks in a set of pastels and paper to dabble in art. I think it would be fun to draw antique pick-up trucks.

"See, I am doing a new thing! Now it springs up; do you not perceive it? I am making a way in the desert and streams in the wasteland." Isaiah 43:19*

---

* NIV

Looking back through my journals, I went through a phase of pretending my husband was somebody else; a mechanism that worked great – for a while. I reasoned that if I was *assigned* to take care of an elderly gentleman with increasing dementia, I could do it; and do it with grace. Thus, I became caregiver to "Mr. Murphy". It seemed easier to understand that Mr. Murphy was once a successful vibrant businessman; looked-up to in his community, a wonderful family man and on and on. It was easier to be kind and patient with him in this light, to feel compassion for him and create ways to bring joy into his day; to make him feel loved. If Mr. Murphy could *see* me, and we stuck to a routine each day, he was very content, agreeable and cheerful. If he did become agitated and cross, I could let it go. After all, he was Mr. Murphy – not my husband, but my *calling*.

Somehow, it made my job easier to separate myself from my husband of over sixty years. Of the guy I dated and traveled with. The one that I shared a life of adventure with. A life of gatherings and picnics and family reunions. Of building houses and working side by side in our business. Of raising our sons together, celebrating weddings and grandbabies. Of exploring amazing places around the world. Of sharing together in ministry. Church every Sunday, after a stop at Dunkin Donuts. A lifetime of memories – slipping away.

At a later entry, *reality* must have set in. I wrote: "I could just pound Mr. Murphy, right into the ground! That cantankerous old goat is driving me up the wall." I decided then, to pretend *I* was someone else. . . . . .

"A bad attitude is like a flat tire. Until you change it, you're not going to get anywhere!"

In this caregiving adventure, there seem to be a million episodes that are beyond description. Constant mood changes keep me on my toes. I'm nervous prior to any get-together with others, anxious about how he will act or what he will say. Before this disease began altering his mind, he was known as the nicest guy in the world. He was kind, loving, generous, polite. One of the things that first attracted me to him, in addition to all those traits, was how loving and caring he was of his family. People here at the retirement community, never knew that about him. Much of the time he's rude and offensive – even to me – in front of others. I suppose it's a sub-conscious device to cover his own lacking. Sometimes when we're with others, he remains quiet, grumpy and remote. At other times, he'll monopolize the conversation with abstract prattle. Our family and close friends understand, but it's still annoying. Other people simply don't get it.

Books on the matter, often suggest the caregiver discuss with the patient, his illness. How he feels about it. Are they kidding? My dear husband has no idea anything is wrong with him!

He must know subconsciously at times, that he's not quite on top of his game. But if I tried to visit with him about his dementia, he would tell me I didn't know what I was talking about.

The same books encourage social interaction for the caregiver and the patient as well. Why? Why put us both in that miserable position? It causes anxiety for both of us! I try for compromise. There are dozens of activities and outings offered here, where we live. We generally attend dinner and music night on Monday, and dinner and movie night on Friday. It's always with the same (understanding) couple, who are fun and easy going. After two years, he never remembers who they are.

"Lord, when doubts fill my mind, when my heart is in turmoil – quiet me, give me renewed hope and cheer." Psalms 94:19

* TLB

The other day a new commercial came on Pandora, my smart phone radio station. It was for the air-freshening product, Fabreze. (By the way, a good thing to have on hand.) Lovely voices rang out, "I love you. . . . . but sometimes you stink!" I spewed my coffee out, laughing. The two essential ingredients to your sanity in being a full-time caregiver, is deep faith and a sense of humor.

Every single day, my husband will say or do the craziest things. I'm training myself to see the humor — even though the circumstances are sad. My sons must have inherited their sense of humor from his side of the family. My side was serious much of the time; all business. I try to filter the incident or the dialogue through the eyes of my sons. They see humor in everything. When he walks out of the bedroom literally half dressed — one half or the other — instead of scolding and ordering — I must laugh. He usually laughs too, even though he doesn't know why. If I see a comic strip that reminds me of *us*, I will cut it out, take a snap and send it to my sons.

The other day we were arguing. (sometimes I forget, it's the number one rule – Do not argue!) He said, "Call Doreen!" I said, "I AM Doreen." He narrowed his eyes and said, "Oh no you're not!" It's a sad commentary on one hand, but I couldn't help but laugh. I reasoned it was a compliment. The cranky old lady arguing with him, couldn't possibly be his sweet wife.

"A cheerful heart is good medicine, but a broken spirit saps a person's strength." Proverbs *17:22**

---

* NLT

Alcoholics Anonymous, has a saying, "Let go and Let God." That's a dandy. I need to remind myself of that all-day long. At this stage, the poor man doesn't do anything right! I must *let it go.* It's one of the hardest parts of caregiving. It's like having a child, except that children learn, improve; do better next time. Watching the growth of a child is beautiful. In our case honey, the "child" we're caring for can't get better. As he declines, he might do it right – now and then, but overall, he is losing those skills.

At this moment, I hear him in the bedroom. He just got up. Drawers are opening and closing – he's attempting to get dressed. No telling what he'll appear in. Probably a weird combination of his Sunday best and yesterday's stained sweatpants. He needs a shower. For now, I will let it go.

In a bit, he will settle in his chair, in his crazy outfit, and "read" the paper. The daily paper is his security blanket of sorts. It tells him what day it is. Most of the time he reads it from beginning to end, sometimes aloud – to me. He can read fairly well, but without comprehension. For instance, he will read the words of a calamity somewhere in the world and chuckle! I want to yell at him for making fun of a thousand people that died in an earthquake. His former self would be aghast. He just doesn't get it. I must let it go.

Last night, as predicted, he was awful to our friends when we picked them up for dinner. He was rude and hateful, mad because they were joining us. He only wants to be with me. They are kind sweet folks and understand. But it was horrible for me. Until dessert, he was ornery to everyone. Even after we got home and he switched personalities to constantly telling me he loved me, (forgetting we had gone out) I couldn't let it go.

"In the end, just three things matter: How well we lived. How well we loved. How well we have learned to let go." Jack Kornfield

In addition to general hygiene, there are a variety of other less pleasant duties that he can no longer do for himself. His hearing is already bad, so keeping ear wax at a minimum is necessary. After a shower is a good time to gently remove what I can. Sometimes Hydrogen Peroxide drops help, but every few months I take him to Immediate Care, to have his ears flushed out. He wears hearing aids, which must be cleaned out and new batteries installed every week. Periodically, it's necessary to have them checked and cleaned professionally.

Fingernails and toenails need to be regularly trimmed, which works best after soaking. He rather enjoys "manicures and pedicures" here at home. Because of fungus, we started out having his toenails trimmed by a foot doctor, but I invested in heavy duty nail cutters and saved the hassle and cost of going.

I also invested in a hair clipper kit that includes an electric nose-hair trimmer, that works with ear-hair too. Once every three weeks, we go to the barber shop where he's been getting his hair cut for years. It's familiar, comfortable and just down the street – a fine ice cream parlor! In between haircuts, I trim the edges and keep his neck shaved.

Being a caregiver has its drawbacks for sure. But it has its rewards too. The word for today: Hang in there sister!

"Love is beautiful when it is professed, but it's only meaningful when it is practiced." B. Brown

It may be necessary as time goes by, to develop a thick skin. When my husband has his back against the wall, probably feeling frustrated that he can't remember; that he doesn't know what's going on, he will sometimes lash out at me. Ninety percent of the time, he's loving and sweet, overly so. But when he's frustrated, he will say "You just get out of here!" or "You don't know anything!" One of his favorites, "This is *my* house (or car, or bed, or sweater) and I will do whatever I want!"

It's one of the most difficult matters to deal with, to overlook, to remain quiet; to let it go. When this happens, in my mind, it's coming from my husband. The one I used to know. In his right mind, he would never say these things. It takes willpower to move on, to not let it affect the rest of my day. A few minutes later, he won't remember any of it, while I am still hurt.

Like every aspect of this disease, it's harder and has more impact on me when I'm tired. In the morning, I might even mimic him and make him laugh. But at night when my nerves are shot and my body tired, I feel like smacking him when he says those hurtful things.

It would be easy to lash out (and sadly, I have at times) but bite your tongue and move on. Maybe change the subject, change the channel, fix him a dish of ice cream, make a cup of tea and put your feet up, say a prayer.

"Sometimes even to live is an act of courage."
Seneca

Make a list of fun things you can do together.
These are some from mine:

Go to the movies occasionally,
if not violent or in 3D.
Go to (the limited) places he enjoys
eating – for early dinner, 3:00 to 4:00.
Take a country drive, listening to his
favorite music. (Elvis Gospel)
Take a daytrip to a lake or water-
fall, go for a short hike.
Enjoy the grandchildren's activities,
mainly sports events.
Go out for ice cream. His fave, a
Mini-Blizzard from Dairy Queen.
Visit a playground or other place
where lots of kids are around.
Attend church, even if he sleeps
through it, he loves to go.
Go to Barnes and Noble, where we
share a coffee and browse the books.
Take a trip down memory lane, driving
through his old neighborhood.
Meet a family member for a latte.

I can think of dozens of things *I'd* like to do; try new restaurants, go to the library, or to a museum. He used to love museums, especially about the Oregon Trail and the Western Frontier. But not anymore. In days' past, we liked to take driving trips, but I discovered the hard way, overnight stays don't work anymore. Case in point, we were staying at a motel in Idaho and I had taken a sleeping pill because of a seven-hour drive ahead the next day. When I woke up, clothes were piled all around the room. Someone else's clothes! Not only that, two men's watches! I have no idea to this day, if he was walking the halls in his pajamas or where the clothes came from. I folded all the garments and placed them in dresser drawers along with the watches, then emailed the manager, explaining what had happened. We headed out of town, leaving a message for our family still in Idaho, "See you back in Oregon. We are on the lam."

"Healing isn't returning to the way things were before. Healing leads to something new." Steven Koski

_____

_____

_____

_____

_____

_____

_____

_____

_____

_____

_____

_____

_____

_____

_____

_____

_____

Make a list of things YOU would like to do, without him. It happens rarely because it takes arrangements that alter other's schedules. I am contemplating the idea of having someone from Home Health Care visit him for an hour occasionally. I know he won't like it, but for my own health it would be a good idea. My list includes:

Lunch with friends or family, trying new places.
Browsing shops – leisurely.
Taking an art class, trying Thai Chi.
Browsing the middle of Costco. (instead of tearing around the perimeter)
Walking outside. (we did together for years, but now he's suffers sciatica)
Get a haircut, pedicure or massage.
Coffee with the ladies in our building.
Attend a Bible Study.

The limited times I *have* been away from him, I've worried the whole time. *What if he gets away? What if he needs to go to the bathroom? What if he's worried about me? What if he's wondering if I'm gone for good?* (he thinks that, even when he can't see me around the house) Despite being with one of our sons, he's likely to have an anxiety attack.

It's obvious (and all the books say so) caregivers need a break. What I've tried to accomplish, is giving myself breaks, even while sitting in the same room with him. It's not quite the same, but it helps immensely. As I've said, writing fiction is therapy for me. Usually I can write sitting next to him, as long as the tennis channel is on and a cozy fire in the fireplace. Writing takes me away – into the lives of the wonderful people I've made up. Of course, all of this is subject to interruption; sometimes constant. I take what I can get!

"Although the world is full of suffering, it is also full of the overcoming of it." Helen Keller

Every minute of every hour of every day, we must make choices. We are free to choose love and free to choose joy. We can choose peace. We can choose to be patient and kind. Goodness is a choice, and faithfulness and gentleness. We can choose self-control. But what I've realized, I cannot successfully make these choices *stick*, without help from God.

It's in the Bible. In Galatians 5:22 it says, *"But the fruits of the spirit are love, joy, peace, longsuffering, kindness, goodness, faithfulness and self-control."*

I would be remiss not to stress, that without my faith in God, this job of caregiver would be impossible. My strength and courage come from Him. My security comes from Him. He is my Rock when I'm wavering; my Shelter in every storm. I begin and end the day talking to Him. And throughout the day He settles me with calmness. I love to read the Psalms and other scripture and I find inspiration in my stack of devotionals.

You may feel cheated because fate has dealt you this hand. It's not what you had planned on. Life as you knew it, is over. It's unfair. Listen honey, you are right where God wants you. There is no other circumstance that will change you from the inside out. He is working to transform you; to change your way of thinking. This journey will bring you to your knees and deepen your faith like no other.

The books are right, we caregivers need to eat right, get good sleep and exercise. But often the missing ingredient is "soul health" – nurturing our spirit; walking with God, one half day at a time.

"There's a choice you have to make in everything you do. So, keep in mind that in the end, the choice you make, makes you." John Wooden

Exercise, as much and as often as possible; together. One of the great advantages of living in a retirement community like ours, is the opportunity to work-out. Many classes are offered at various levels in the fitness studio, with qualified instructors. For us, the best option is the weight room, right down the hall. We can pick and choose our timing, so most always have the place to ourselves in a room full of cardio equipment overlooking the picturesque Deschutes River. In addition to a universal gym, there are a variety of weight machines and free weights as well as yoga mats and fitness balls. We can turn on the music we like and go at our own pace. Although my husband used to be a runner and played tennis until recently, he's sometimes ready to quit before I am, but is content to sit at one of the weight stations and watch until I finish.

For many years, we walked together, annually participating in a 5K for charity. Two years ago, when we first moved here, we walked two to four miles along the river trail several times a week. Last fall he developed a painful sciatica which has limited walking outside. Otherwise that would be my first choice. If possible, develop the habit of walking together – outdoors. Even fifteen minutes. You will be able to do more and more as time goes by, but just get started. Today.

Besides the proven health benefits of exercise, you both will feel energized and sleep better. It's an activity you can do together near home or at a beautiful park. And while you're at it, observe God's Creation all around you. Each season brings a wealth of incredible sights to your surroundings.

Besides all that, walking keeps your weight under control – to counteract those ice cream dates!

"Live life in radical amazement; get up in the morning and look at the world in a way that takes nothing for granted!" AJ Heschel

Grocery shopping is becoming more challenging as time goes by. We purposely shop at a supermarket that features a coffee shop, chairs and tables surrounding a cozy fireplace - located near checkout. For the past several years, my husband was content to sit there with a coffee and the newspaper. Those days are gone. I will try it on occasion but end up looking for him out in the parking lot! So now he goes with me up and down the aisles, him pushing the cart. At the halfway point, he's quite uncomfortable with his sciatica. There's no good answer. I've changed my mode of operation, shopping once a week for a short list of necessities, written per map of the store.

I'm working on a solution to have our granddaughter scheduled for coffee with gramps at the grocery store, on a day that works for her. That would give us a chance to catch-up with her and I could speed-shop while she continued the visit with her grandfather.

One of the benefits of limited shopping, is that instead of running all over town for birthday, wedding, baby and Christmas gifts, (which would be impossible) I can do it at the supermarket. Gift cards of all kinds and greeting cards are the way to go. Last Christmas, I purchased twenty attractive coffee mugs (they came in cute boxes) and a gift card to put in each one, all from the market.

I have left suggestions at various establishments around town, proposing that more women would shop longer, if there was a comfortable seating area for husbands. (with or without dementia) I wish someone would invent a grocery cart/wheelchair, that he could enjoy the ride, while I added items in an attached cart.

"We make a living by what we get. We make a life by what we give." Winston Churchill

Caregiving in and of itself, is not all that difficult. Except for this one thing: Life goes on. No matter how organized, how prepared and how you've simplified; stuff happens. He keeps saying, "I LOVE you" in a kind of sing-songy way, over and over and over. It requires an answer. "I love you too!" You're chopping onions. You cut your finger. "I LOVE you", he says again. Your finger is bleeding. You grab for a paper towel and knock an egg on the floor. "I LOVE you." grrrrr "I love you too!"

Sometimes he gets on a roll with "You are so bee-uuu-tee-full!" "Well, I haven't got fixed up yet honey." "You are so bee-uuu-tee-full!" The phone rings. It's the bank. "You are so bee-uuu-tee-full!" "My account is overdrawn? That's impossible. We just made a deposit." "You are so bee-uuu-tee-full!" "Eastside branch, drive-through." (later discover deposit over the visor in car) I can't think straight half the time myself.

Now you would reason that I'd feel extra blessed to have him say those things to me. I know he really means it too because he says them in his sleep. But twenty-seven times in less than a five-minute period drives me nuts! It's more prevalent toward evening. I've found it works best to put away my projects and sit by him to watch a ballgame on TV. If *I* get into it (the basketball or tennis or whatever is on) he will begin to focus more on the TV.

The experts say that often toward evening, is when people suffering dementia become more aggressive or intense. They call it "sun-downing". My husband is more likely to increase his rambling. He will go on and on about nothing is seems, but probably in his mind he knows what he's trying to say. To me it's more like this: "Remember how we always went there and that guy wanted us to come over and we got a lot of money on it and you were there too! Remember?" (trust me, this example is the short version) I usually say, "Hmmm. Interesting." Or "I kinda remember. Hmmm."

"Scared is what you're feeling. Brave is what you're doing." Emma Donoghue

I was born and raised a picky housekeeper. In earlier times, whenever I would vacuum under my husband's feet, or keep him off a just-mopped floor he would ask, "Are you expecting the Queen?" and I would say, "She's already here."☺ The thing is, I would keep things clean and tidy even if I lived alone in a mountain cabin. In this caregiving business, I'm learning to compromise. If the beds are made, the kitchen is in order, the bathroom clean and the house smells fresh, I can let dusting, vacuuming, mopping the floors go — for a while.

I love living in smaller quarters. After maintaining much larger homes over the years, it's a wonderful benefit, living in a retirement complex. I wash sheets frequently, and give extra attention to the bathroom, especially around the toilet. It is necessary to wash the contour rug every other day, rotating with a clean one. I spot the carpeting as needed, and keep a glass pie plate filled with vinegar, under the dresser and charcoal odor absorbers concealed throughout the house. (Some mornings the bedroom smells like a cross between an outhouse and men's locker room) Obviously keeping my husband clean is paramount to keeping the house fresh.

If you are a picky housekeeper sweetie, lower your standards, let some things go; change your perspective. Ask yourself, does that really need to be done? And while you're at it, apply this principal to other areas of your life. Last week, when I cut my finger chopping an onion and knocked at egg on the floor, I was preparing my signature dish for a potluck. After all, everyone expects a great dish from me. Really? I now have a new plan for the next potluck. Next time, I will pick up a veggie tray on my way, or even better ask someone else to do it and pay them at the party. It's back to basics; change your way of thinking. You have your hands full and besides; veggies are good for everyone.

"Reverence for God adds hours to each day!" Proverbs 10:27*

* TLB

_____

_____

_____

_____

_____

_____

_____

_____

_____

_____

_____

_____

_____

_____

Palliative Care is what we're doing; keeping the recipient of our care comfortable and content. It means if they were diagnosed with a terminal illness, there would be no treatment given. Consequently, there are choices to be made to that end of keeping him comfortable and content.

The man used to love vegetables. He's the one that got me liking Brussel Sprouts! That was way back. These days, he won't eat his vegetables. Period. He never liked starches, potatoes, rice, pasta; none of it. I don't worry about a balanced diet, but one he enjoys and one that keeps him regular. His morning oatmeal is not just oatmeal. It includes walnuts, almonds, blueberries, dried cranberries and a little brown sugar. Half the time he enjoys cold cereal, two kinds combined with granola. It's always topped with bananas, blueberries, raspberries and during the summer fresh peaches. He eats a large bowl, with two cups skim milk. He seems to love his breakfast.

For dinner, he likes to eat salmon or chicken with no vegetables or starch. The only exception, baked yams with butter and brown sugar, sliced avocado or sometimes a small Caesar salad. He likes mild chili, chicken chili and baked beans. Our Sunday night special is peanut butter and jelly sandwiches on whole grain bread. He doesn't like water, but he loves flavored fizzy water and drinks lots of it. If I think it's necessary, I treat him with an afternoon "cocktail" of half prune juice and half apple juice. He takes a daily multivitamin. Except for the lack of vegetables, he eats relatively well. Of course, there's the ice cream. Every evening between dinner and bedtime, he really enjoys a dish of low-fat Butter Pecan and a couple of cookies.

"You can't judge people if you are too busy trying to love them." Mother Teresa

Other people for the most part – don't get it. If we are attending a social event, rather it's friends or family, someone always says, "Your husband is doing great!" (I think it's meant to encourage me.) Behind the scenes, he's having an anxiety attack. He refuses anything to eat or drink and is usually ready to go home five minutes after we get there. He doesn't know who anybody is – but tries to fake it. Sometimes.

He looks good, he's clean – his clothes are clean, hair trimmed, face shaved. He smells good. It's not by accident. Sometimes I want to say, "Do you know what it took to get here? He only *appears* like a person who has it all together, because I got him that way!" They have no idea. They have no idea that after he was completely showered, shaved and dressed – he went back into the bathroom (while I was getting my clothes on) and lathered up his head with shaving cream and sprayed bathroom deodorizer on his face. Another fifteen minutes to soak his head and face and replace his wet shirt with a clean one.

For me, it's a matter of being cordial to others, try to maintain a conversation and never take my eyes off him. In unfamiliar places, if he needs to use the bathroom, rather than ask where it is, he will wander outside and go in the yard. I try to stay ahead of it, get him to the bathroom and come prepared with "Wet Ones" to clean his hands, and make it a habit to check the guest bathroom after he comes out.

One suggestion is to carry pre-made cards that explain, "My husband has dementia", or something to that effect. I haven't tried this yet, but I can think of other ways to use them, like at stores and restaurants. On occasion, he has come out of a store with something in his pocket.

"God did not call His children to a playground, but to a battleground." Billy Graham.

_____

_____

_____

_____

_____

_____

_____

_____

_____

_____

_____

_____

_____

_____

To keep a peaceful atmosphere, I orchestrate our schedule in a way that puts space between events. A day *on* and a day *off* so to speak. I never make appointments before noon, to let my husband sleep-in (his best sleep), eat a good unrushed breakfast and go through the shower process. Things like teeth cleaning at the dentist and eye checks I try to schedule for the two of us, back to back, in the same block of time. We would be going together either way. It might be errands and shopping or getting the car serviced or a scenic drive. Occasionally, we go to a movie. We usually eat an early dinner out on those days, somewhere easy and spend the evening at home.

On the off day, we stay home mostly, close around our retirement complex. On home days, morning goes the same as the above (but let the shower go) and at noon, we work-out together in the weight room down the hall. Occasionally we meet friends in the lobby for coffee and a visit. In good weather, we walk outside in as much as he feels like it. On Fridays, we have a standing date with another couple for "dinner and movie" night. On the weekends, we often spend time with family and Sunday mornings ride the retirement bus to church. Every morning, we read — my reading aloud to him, from two inspirational books and the Bible. In fact, we just completed the entire Bible, Old and New Testament in a little less than two years. Half the time, he falls asleep but that's okay. He loves my reading and it's a relaxing time for me.

Our schedule of course, is sometimes interrupted, but maintaining a routine for the most part, keeps us both calmer and more collected. And by the way, instead of fifteen minutes' margin time for appointments, allow for thirty and maybe end up with fifteen. It's better to get there, find a parking spot and have time to relax in the waiting room. Rushing rattles his cage. Mine too!

"Keep calm and carry on."

A very real fact of life is – death. Plan for it; get your affairs in order. A while back, our son brought to my attention that eighty percent or more of caregivers die before the person they are caring for! He gently presented the question of what I would do if that happened. (I smiled to myself thinking, 'No dear. What would _you_ do?") You will feel better once you have contacted a good estate planning attorney to help you with the process.

You'll need an updated Will, an Advanced Directive and Power of Attorney. The first file in our filing cabinet is labeled "End of Life" and I have advised our three sons of its location. It includes the above documents, banking information, contents of safe box, passwords, and pre-written obituaries with updated photographs. I have written a very short note to my husband, should I go first. I can picture him carrying it around in his pocket. My next move is to secure burial sites and start a payment plan.

I confess all of this has a little to do with my being a control freak – even after I'm gone! But there is something very settling and comforting to know you are not leaving your kids with a mess.

You may be wondering how I accomplished all this while caring full time for my husband. He just went with me and commented 'that was the sweetest little girl', who happened to be our attorney. He is less intimidated by soft-spoken women.

"Your children are always your babies, even if they have gray hair." Janet Leigh

Earlier I mentioned the idea of "Pleasant Inns" along the way. This is a time in history of bad news continually bombarding us. The fact that it's so *in our face* in this generation, makes it even worse. There have always been wars and atrocities, hunger and homelessness. Circumstances in your own life, in addition to the hard burden of caring for someone with dementia, it can all weigh you down. Your own mental health is at stake. We caregivers must work at not going crazy ourselves.

"Mere Christianity" by CS Lewis is one of my all-time favorite books. Not just a good read, it has made me stronger and wiser. I read sections of it over and over. The idea of Pleasant Inns is Lewis' idea. Life is hard, but in every new day – no matter what – if you seek for, you will find, treasures along the way. Your busy-ness and stress may distract, but those Pleasant Inns are there. Honey, you must take time to smell the roses.

There is always something to marvel at outdoors. In Central Oregon, deer roam outside our window nearly every day. We have a pond, now frozen, that will soon inhabit ducks and the nightly music of frogs. Seasons are very distinctive here and soon we will watch spring buds pop out on dead Aspen trees. Inside, I create my own Pleasant Inns. They are like little rewards; hot coffee, the comics, good books, music, a catnap, a cup of tea, a phone call or email. Simple things no longer taken for granted. I may be in my rubber gloves doing the morning tasks, but at the end is my reward, my Pleasant Inn. After all, I only need to make it to noon. Then I start over, with the second half day.

*"How can a woman be wise? The only way to begin is by reverence for God!" Psalms 111:10**

---

* TLB

Let's take a page to summarize:

1. Change your perspective
2. Don't argue
3. Develop a thick skin
4. Look for solutions
5. Address driving issues sooner rather than later
6. Simplify, simplify, simplify
7. Discover a new thing for yourself
8. Develop a sense of humor
9. Let it go!
10. Make a list of activities to do together
11. Exercise together
12. Develop a routine – control schedule
13. Take care of your own health
14. Get your affairs in order
15. Look for "Pleasant Inns"
16. Seek guidance from God

In the uncertainty of the disease of dementia, there are no cut and dried answers. Maybe this list will help – one half day at a time.

"Certainty is overrated." Brian McLaren

My doctor mentioned a while back, there are some medications out now, to slow the progress of Alzheimer's Disease. After a brief conversation, I asked her why anyone would want to do that, especially in later stages. She agreed that for my husband's case it would only (maybe) slow the agony for both of us. The pills aren't guaranteed to work in any case.

Although it may sound unkind, in some areas as things get *worse*, they get *better*. The more he retreats into oblivion the less frustrated and agitated he is over certain things. He's a little less mad about taking a shower now – and partly because I've calmed my strategy. For example, instead of saying, "you need to get in the shower" – in which case a fight pursues, it works better to wait until he takes a late morning trip to the bathroom and just follow him in and start helping him take his clothes and shoes off. I have him hold a towel over his face to protect his eyes and while he's sitting in the chair, work shampoo into his hair. Then turn on the shower and walk out, leaving him to take care of business and hopefully get in the shower and wash with soap.

There will come a time, when I will need to scrub his whole body, but for now he does okay and stays in there long enough (singing away) that he must get mostly clean. He's forgotten how to brush his teeth – at least in the normal way. I discovered the reason toothpaste was all over the place and that he ran out frequently, is that in addition to putting it on the brush, he was squeezing it down the entire handle of the toothbrush! So now, when he comes out of the shower, his toothbrush is sitting there – ready to go with toothpaste on the brush part only.

At the urging of my family, a gave him a prescription sleeping pill one night. Stories abound about crazy things people do on Ambien, no matter their mental condition. I learned a hard lesson. Sometime during the night, he thought the kitchen was the bathroom. Before realizing it, I managed to track through a big puddle on the floor, as I crept there in the dark to start my morning coffee!

"If at first you don't succeed, try and try and try – again!"

I hope by now, that life's little pleasures have become more and more meaningful to you; that you're not still trying to cling to the past. For me, early morning time alone, with my coffee, my Bible and devotionals keeps me grounded. I write in my journal every day. Every single day I am inspired, strengthened and encouraged by scripture and daily readings from Billy Graham, Sarah Young, Mike Silva and CS Lewis. Seriously, try it!

When I speak of life's little pleasures, not only am I referring to the things that are enjoyable for me, but the things I can create that bring joy to my husband. Even if his food preferences are limited, I cook what he likes and serve it on our best plates. He always smiles when I deliver his fizzy water in a champagne glass. When I say, "dinner is ready" he is excited to see the table set nicely with a candle or a fresh flower in the center.

He likes when I give him a manicure or play a piece on the piano or sing an old Sunday school song. Sometimes I lead him in a dance on the kitchen floor. He loves it when we drive through Dutch Brothers for an Iced Kicker! He likes to go for drives and stop at parks to watch kids at play. Often while we're driving, I'll start singing along with the CD were listening too and eventually he will too.

It's a natural thing for us women to care for others. If you're thinking, *'give me a break'* I want to encourage you to try it. You may not always get a happy response (my husband usually balks at sitting at the "manicure table" – at first – but ends up, he quite enjoys the pampering!)

"Love has a way of making places sacred and moments meaningful." Janet Hobson

One (half) Day At A Time

_____

_____

_____

_____

_____

_____

_____

_____

_____

_____

_____

_____

_____

_____

No matter how much you simplify, create solutions and keep a routine, life brings events you can't ignore; big occasions to celebrate! Next weekend, we will attend a big family wedding. It will be an elaborate outdoor affair, attended by family and friends – many of whom we haven't seen in a while. We are grandparents of the groom. We will be honored as such as we walk down the aisle. I can't wait for that special day – and yet my stomach hurts with a sense of dread.

We took a drive out to the venue recently, to find out what the bathroom situation is and see the layout in general. It may seem simple to others. Just go and enjoy the day, right? My husband has been wearing sweatpants only for the last two years, because he cannot navigate belts, buckles, buttons and zippers. I discovered that the hard way. The bathroom thing is my biggest worry. I will need to stay ahead of it, as he will be wearing big boy slacks. (Our outfits – head to toe – were all ordered online! Shopping in stores is a thing of the past.)

The celebration also includes rehearsal dinner. Another set of clothes, another set of worries. After all these years of caring for him, I don't know what to expect. He may be loud and outspoken; he may be grumpy and mad the whole time. If he's not attached to me for a minute, he may swipe food from the buffet table and put it in his pocket. If I get distracted – and I will, he might wander off, urinate in a flowerpot or drink someone else's beverage.

My family is willing to step-up at these occasions, but they will all be having their own fun, seeing folks they haven't seen in a while, dancing and enjoying wonderful food and taking care of their kids. I don't expect them to "sit with dad!" I must trust that it will all work out. I will pray and prepare and if need be, we will slip out early. But not until after the *kiss*!

"Life isn't fair. It isn't the way you think it should be. But the way you choose to respond to it, is what makes all the difference." Virginia Satir

For the past few weeks, whenever we go somewhere, my husband insists on directing my driving, gasping loudly if I don't turn where he thinks I should. He has no idea of our destination but gets quite emphatic that I "should have turned there." He likes going for drives in general but doesn't like to stop. When we do stop at a store, a restaurant, one of our family's homes or anywhere, he most often refuses to get out of the car.

It seems logical, just to leave him in the car when that happens. However, several times he has set off the alarm, causing the horn to honk relentlessly. He has gotten into the glove box and lost the registration, proof of insurance and more importantly my Starbuck's card! Worse, he has gotten out of the car and wandered around in the parking lot or into a store, not necessarily the one I'm in.

He's crazy about little kids and if he spots one, wherever we are, he tracks them down and attempts to tell the parents how blessed they are. It's very sweet and his intentions are pure, but most often he bumbles the words he wants to say, and people don't know for sure his intentions. He will approach the same family more than once, not realizing he's already been there and done that. When he's on the loose, that's how I usually find him; talking to the mother of a baby.

The other key to finding him, is - every single day he insists on wearing blue. He loves blue. His closet is full of sweat suits; red, grey, black etc., but he will only wear a blue polo shirt, blue sweatpants, blue jacket and blue running shoes! (The neighbor sarcastically calls him the "bluebird of happiness.") But that *blue* sure helps me find him.

"God help me move beyond my first breath of reaction, and with a second breath, respond from a deeper place of wisdom, strength and love."
Anonymous Prayer

I've let this one-half day project rest a while. Partly due to life's events and summer celebrations. Partly due to burn-out. Reading back through these pages, I realize I don't always practice what I preach. I get tired and frustrated. I don't want to figure out one more solution. I'm tired of rolling up my sleeves and cleaning up messes. I'd just like to go the beach! Today! By myself!

But this too shall pass. An evening walk, a good night's sleep, healthy food, and morning devotions. I'll get past this. Part of my discouragement is due to how things have changed. The recognition that my husband is failing more, going deeper and deeper into the world of dementia.

The greatest change is something new to me, but common to the disease. He has begun suffering Dysphagia – choking during meals, getting food and drink in his windpipe causing a disaster on several occasions while eating out. From researching online, his brain is failing to direct the food to the right place. He's in the early phase — but ultimately could require a feeding tube. Pneumonia is also a threat.

I'm learning that beverages need to be thickened and foods made softer. I need to make sure he's sitting up straight when eating and that he does not lay down for 30 minutes after a meal. The atmosphere needs to be calm; anxiety only adds to the problem. I've made peace with the fact, that we can no longer go out for dinner (or breakfast, or lunch) - it's too risky. We can pick up meals to *go* half the time and I will cook the other half. Overall, things have gotten more difficult, physically, mentally and in all ways. I was beginning to sink in discouragement. Then I read the following quote:

"If you're lucky, God will lead you to a situation you cannot control, you cannot fix, or you cannot even understand. At that point, true spirituality begins, and transformation is possible." Thomas Merton

_____

_____

_____

_____

_____

_____

_____

_____

_____

_____

_____

_____

_____

_____

_____

Often my husband will get up during the night or early morning and get dressed sort of, and make his bed sort of, and sit in the little chair by his bed. For hours. He's awake, sort of – at least his eyes are open, his arms are folded, but I can look at him and get no response. He sits there until I walk right up to him and snap him out of it. On several occasions, he's let out a big sigh of relief, like he thought he'd never see me again. Sometimes he'll say, "I'm just trying to figure out, how to get home." I hate thinking he's afraid or that he doesn't know where he is. It's just another sign of mental decline.

For the second time, he's chewed up his hearing aid. It was a battle getting the pieces out of his mouth, once I figured out what it was. No longer under warranty, I decided to let it go for a while and see if it really made a difference before investing another $2000. Even though on palliative care, I had determined to maintain his eyes, ears and teeth. But it almost seems better without the hearing aid. He's a little less frustrated – hearing less.

He's more inclined toward ornery streaks when we're out in public. It's just that he doesn't know what's going on, so he's on the defense. He wants to go out and is happy in the car – until I turn right - or left - or stop. "What are you DOING?" he asks, and then he's mad and pouty the whole time we're out and wants to go home. After we're settled at home, he'll say, "Want to go somewhere?" Can't win!

The wedding is over, we got through it better than I expected. He did have a choking spell at rehearsal dinner, but not terrible (we got to the bathroom in time) so we didn't eat at the wedding. Friends and family, we haven't seen in a while were kind and gracious and he smiled and laughed and looked like he recognized them. In truth, he couldn't even distinguish most of his own kids and grandkids. Five minutes on the road home, he had no idea we had attended a wedding.

"These troubles and sufferings of ours are, after all, quite small and won't last very long. Yet this short time of distress will result in God's riches blessing upon us forever and ever!" 2 Corinthians 4:17*

---

* TLB

_____

_____

_____

_____

_____

_____

_____

_____

_____

_____

_____

_____

_____

_____

I love "purple socks" day. It's a day I'm not under pressure to go anywhere, or do anything, unless I want to. It's a stay-home day, as if a sudden summer storm or a winter blizzard, forced us to be homebound. My purple socks are my faves. They are old and faded and soft and comfortable. They don't go with anything. It sounds crazy but wearing them – along with perfectly uncoordinated sweats – gives me the feeling that I can let down a little. At the end of the day, it's not much different than any other day. The same duties are required of me, but I can relax more; maybe let a few things go. My purple socks give me permission. It's more of a psychological thing.

The combination of summer events (even minimal involvement) and my husband failing more and more, has taken its toll on me. Even after a decent night's sleep, some mornings I can hardly drag myself out of bed. Not often, but sometimes I get up with the feeling like I must conquer Mt. Everest. You know what I mean? That sweet little old man will wake up and shuffle out in a while and a kind of dread will overcome me. Can I do this one more day? Can I muster up strength and patience? Sweetness? Energy? The Bible says, "With God all things are possible." So, I say a prayer and put on my purple socks. I will admonish myself to 'take it easy; don't sweat the small stuff.'

What would I do today, if we were snowed in? Maybe make granola? Or dig out an old photo album? Or perhaps read aloud to my husband? (it doesn't matter if he falls asleep) This day holds a pile of blessings. Look for them; write them in your journal. Take the day off girl – at least in your mind. "Rainy days and Mondays" aren't really all that bad.

"If you're going to climb Mt. Everest, make sure you bring the flag!" Mike Silva

One (half) Day At A Time

Perhaps you're deliberating about a memory care facility at some point and wondering why I've not mentioned it. Here, where we live, several levels of care are available including memory care. We live in the independent living part of the campus. We can only live here because of my full-time caring for my husband. I must keep track of him, make sure he doesn't "get out" or cause disruption of any kind, here in independent living. Another building on campus offers assisted living, more for physical care needs. There are various levels of in-home care available as well.

In memory care, the patient lives full time in a secured memory care unit with a community of dementia patients. The care is highly rated, with a more than adequate number of well-trained staff people. Friends and family often ask, "when" will I decide it's time to move my husband to memory care. The fact is, without long term health-care insurance, it's very expensive. In all honesty, I can't afford it. In all honesty, I couldn't do it – right now – even if I had the financial ability. Despite the fact, he can be a pill at times, my husband still knows me and loves me. He wants to be with me; and very unhappy when he's not.

I've learned from others who volunteer in memory care, some patients can still play bingo and participate in certain activities like crafts. My husband is past that; he would not fit in that category. He truly can't do anything – but read and watch TV – with very little understanding.

I get that things can change in an instant. My health may fail, or I may go on to glory first. If so, our pay-down investment to live in independent living is 90% refunded. That amount would take care of him in memory care for a couple of years. Medicare does not cover long term care, but I understand, in some cases, they will cover two months of in-home care during the transition time.

"I can do all things in Him who strengthens me." Philippians 4:13*

---

* RSV

As I've mentioned before, the thing that really helps and keeps me from going over the edge, is my morning-time routine – coffee, devotionals, Bible and journal. For the current year, my journals include Jesus Always, by Sarah Young, Mornings with Tozer, Mike Silva's Word for You today, Hope for Each Day by Billy Graham and A Year with CS Lewis. There are lots of options, some I read again each year. I look up corresponding scriptures in a Life Application Bible – an easy-to-read version. Then I pray, sometimes in writing and add an entry to my journal. It takes an hour or sometimes two, beginning around 6:30. My husband gets his best sleep during this time. Like I've said, it's prime time for me!

Another big boost is *music* throughout the day, at home or in the car. Recently, driving to a family event about twenty miles away, we took back roads and listened to an old CD. It was transforming. We both started out on the cranky side – the getting ready, an exhausting ordeal – but by the time we arrived at our destination our moods had elevated considerably. It helped that we traveled through beautiful country; white mountains, blue skies and tall timbers. But *music* made the difference.

Some days I choose a theme song for that day, with the idea of purposely getting it stuck in my head. It might be a hymn, or praise song or maybe a folk or country song or perhaps an oldie. One that lifts the spirit. One that applies to my circumstances. Some of my favorite oldies were hits during wartime. Here is a great example from the 1940's:

"You've got to –
     Accentuate the positive,
     Eliminate the negative,
     Latch on to the affirmative,
     And don't mess with Mr. In-between."

     Amen.

It seems a lot of models, actresses and performers experience "wardrobe malfunctions" these days! My husband, dressing himself in the morning – brings new meaning to the term. Oh my. When he's had a good shower the afternoon before, and it's a stay-at-home day, I let it go and see what happens. At this point, all underwear is eliminated. Sometimes, after emptying half his closet, he will put one polo-type shirt on top of another, two or three – all blue. Maybe add a jacket and always socks, (most often not matching) and his blue running shoes. There have been times when he's appeared with *nothing* on in-between the layered top and blue shoes! Or sometimes two pair of pants and nothing but a jacket on top. There is no rhyme or reason.

As far as his ensemble from the day before, it is necessary to wash all of it. Urine leaks can go undetected sometimes, but I found out the hard way, not to put worn clothing back in the closet – even if it looks good; as if it could go another day. My rule of thumb, wash everything, every day to eliminate the possibility of odors. It's easy to become insensitive to odors in your own home.

The other rule of thumb, is not to react to his crazy outfit and wardrobe malfunctions, only assist putting on the pants he forgot, until later in the day, adjusting what I can for going to the weight-room or out to get the mail.

Every other day, the days we go out – even if he's spent a chunk of time getting dressed I will *scheme* to get him in the shower and once he's in there, lay out fresh clothes for the day, clean shirt, pants, underwear and socks – on the bed. It is necessary to help him with each part, adding deodorant and helping him shave. (He shaves a dozen times during the day *and* night with his electric razor – but misses a few spots.) Through this whole process, a sense of humor is necessary!

"It is bad to suppress laughter. It goes back down and spreads to your hips." Fred Allen

When we took care of my mother-in-law, during the time from when her husband died in 1995, until she died in 2001, there was very little in the way of help for caregivers, concerning dementia. One book had been recommended, <u>The Thirty-Six Hour Day</u>, by Nancy L. Mace and Peter V. Rabins. It's still available and quite helpful. Nowadays, there are many more resources – in fact somewhat overwhelming. Who of us caregivers have time to find the best help? But one of the most helpful I've discovered, is <u>Learning to Speak Alzheimer's</u> by Joanne Koenig Coste.

Another resource is in the form of DVD's, by Teepa Snow. A highly educated woman in the field and wonderful teacher. I must agree with her many five-star reviews on Amazon. The tape I ordered is entitled "It's All in Your Approach" – reinforcing my own experience - ways of changing me, the caregiver; because the person with dementia cannot change. Teepa Snow's programs are available through Online Video Viewing as well. The videotaping is not super professional, but the teaching makes up for it.

There's a wealth of material and blogs on the Internet by family caregivers and professionals as well. It would be easy to become overwhelmed and bogged down with information. Search for specific aid, but remember honey, mostly it can't be fixed. What *will* help though, is changing the way you think about it; figuring out a solution and persevering.

"Perseverance is the hard work you do after you get tired of doing the hard work you already did." Newt Gingrich

As the one you are caring for declines, you will need to reinforce care of yourself. Now that my husband and I are no longer eating out, I've come to realize in my preparing meals for him – soft foods, thicker drinks, because of the choking problem – I've slacked off about my own eating habits. (I can always grab cold cereal, right?) Make a comprehensive grocery list including things you can both enjoy but adding fresh veggies and fruit and lean meats for yourself.

Eating out has been one of our greatest pleasures in all the years of our marriage. It's what you do on a date night. It's what you do when you meet people. It's what you do when there's a celebration or family get-together. But we can no longer do that. You may have to give it up eventually too. But remember – think "solutions"! Who would guess, *ice cream* would be a solution? Recently we attended a family picnic. We ate first at home and arrived late on purpose. We could still enjoy a little ice cream and the fun of watching our grandkids blast each other with water balloons! If my husband is sitting up straight, ice cream seems to work fine.

Rather than being disappointed about not eating out, I've started coming up with ideas to prepare things that *I* enjoy. All my years of cooking I realize, has mainly been what he likes. Sometimes I call ahead to one of our favorite spots and order something to go, just for me. (while his soup simmers in the crockpot) It's OK to do that. Sometimes I order double and put half in the freezer.

As far as my own health, I know at some point I need to get out – get a break from the intensity of this caregiver job. I decided to bite the bullet and set up an appointment with a Home Care gal, here where we live. This first time will simply be a thirty-minute visit – her, him and me. When she leaves, I will send with her a one-page outline of his needs and what to expect when she comes next time, to stay with him for an hour, while I go for a long walk – by myself.

"Cooking done with care is an act of love."
Craig Claiborne

If you haven't discovered yet, this job of caregiver can be gross. As things digress, normal body functions begin to fail, fungus begins to develop in toenails and fingernails. (This part of the disease is not as difficult for me as the loss of mental reasoning and logical thinking.) The choking is worse than vomiting in a way because it's mostly phlegm and undigested food that comes up. Sometimes gross stuff is under the fingernails. When I was a kid and would spend the night with my friend Marlene, her mother always made us scrub our hands first thing in the morning. It's a good habit to develop for anyone.

As far as dealing with the unpleasant things of caregiving, the only alternative to doing it yourself, would be to hire a nurse. Or better yet, *become* one. It's a mechanism – like taking care of Mr. Murphy. I sometimes *pretend* I'm a nurse. In fact, I've ordered a pair of scrubs. Have you seen how cute they are these days? And they come in a bunch of colors. I've ordered blue – my husband's favorite and next time, maybe purple. To go with my purple socks.

Some things seem to get better, easier, as the patient declines – as bad as that may sound. The issue of embarrassment over having to help them in the bathroom, in the shower or sponge bath, slowly fades, along with their memory. Over time they are no longer ashamed or self-conscious of having to be physically cared for.

I've learned it's possible to condition yourself to handle whatever is required in caregiving. It's mind over matter. It's imagining you're a nurse, pulling on your bright blue scrubs, putting on some lipstick and going to work. You can do it! – one half day at a time.

"Always wash your hands first-thing in the morning. You never know where they've been during the night!" Mrs. Reinika

Recently, in Mike Silva's devotional, he quoted from a well-known expert, the following: *"Don't just change your circumstances to improve your life — change yourself to improve your circumstances!"* I love that. It's the premise of this journal, the thing I've tried to convey. The expert goes on to say, *"Don't see change as something hard that must be done — see it as something helpful that can be done! Pursue it!"*

In this position of caregiver, it's about changing me; changing my perspective. I must *pursue* change. My husband cannot.

Some days it seems impossible to change my thinking and to change my approach. I forget that my purpose and priority is taking care of my husband; that my "job" is Jerry. This assignment takes energy, strength and discipline. It takes patience, kindness and sweetness. It takes grace. I cannot do it on my own, but only with the help of God. My trust is not in myself, but in him.

I admit to being frustrated and flustered at times, over-tired and cranky — especially at the end of the day. When I'm in that state, with my back against the wall, my patience growing thin, I must stop, take a deep breath and pray. "Let go and let God." Often that includes an apology to my poor husband who was on the receiving end of my wrath. Even though he will forget quickly, I won't. I will fall in bed feeling a failure. But God heals and forgives. And tomorrow is a new day. I will pray and pursue change. Change in myself, to improve my circumstances. It can be done, one choice at a time; one half day at a time.

"The power of prayer doesn't depend upon the virtue of the one who prays, but on the unchanging love of the One who hears." Unknown

_____

_____

_____

_____

_____

_____

_____

_____

_____

_____

_____

_____

_____

_____

_____

Every widow I know tells me the same thing. They all say, "well at least you still *have* him!" I understand their loneliness, the longing they may feel when they see us together. Unless their husbands had Alzheimer disease or another form of dementia, unless they've been on this caregiving journey they can't relate to my situation, any more than I relate to theirs. I want to say, "No, I don't truly still have him. He's been gone for a long, long time."

The one I've been married to for over six decades, the father of my children and grandfather of their children, that person is no longer here. It's the 'Long Good-Bye' – like the book about Ronald Reagan. The disease is so gradual. I can't pinpoint when it began. It happens slowly, slowly like he's sinking in mire an inch at a time. The saddest part, I can't quite remember, exactly how he used to be. Going through pictures helps, but they no longer register with him. I say, "Remember when we had that little vacation place? How we took the boys to Sunrise Service on Easter? Remember when we lived at the ranch?"

Earlier on, trying to take him down memory lane, only caused frustration and confusion. Showing pictures from the past, just triggered more bewilderment. These days, he shows little interest in photos, except for Snapchats on my phone of the babies in our family. He's not sure who's they are or who they are, but usually smiles and says, "That's beautiful!" He doesn't' know it's his own great grandchildren.

In all honesty, I have prayed the Lord would take him – sooner, rather than later – for his sake and mine. We believe without a doubt; we will be together in Heaven. It would be such a relief for both of us. But only God knows the number of our days. I shall carry on.

"The prayer that never fails: "Thy will be done."

It's a hundred wonders we haven't caused a wreck. My husband is getting terrible at bursting out with loud proclamations over the least thing, while I'm driving! Like turning left, for example. "WHAT ARE YOU DOING?", he shouts. Or turning right. Or stopping! He wants to go somewhere, until we get on the road. If I hit a chuckhole he goes ballistic. Or else he'll frantically say, "HERE! TURN HERE!" I'll gasp, hit the break, and yell, "DON'T DO THAT!" I'm the jumpy type anyway.

After not driving for several years, he's suddenly forgotten that I'm the designated driver. He's getting more aggressive about getting behind the wheel. He races to get to the driver's side before me. There is no convincing him. I've stood in many a parking lot trying to.

This happened at the family picnic last week. When it was time to leave, he beat me to the driver's side and jumped in! One by one I motioned the others to go ahead, conveying that I would deal with him. When we were finally the last car, with no one to observe, I walked back over to the picnic area and casually sat on a bench, ignoring the stubborn man behind the wheel. (the car-keys are always with me – no danger of him starting the car) Eventually, I hollered over to him 'come on over and sit-down honey'. Slowly he complied and as soon as he did, I took off sprinting for the car, leaping in the driver's seat, slamming and locking the doors. Without hesitation, he walked around to the passenger side, I unlocked the door, he calmly took his seat and buckled up.

It may seem cruel, but the man is beyond reasoning with. I'm tempted to argue, but that does no good either. There are just times for flat-out trickery.

"When at first you don't succeed – try sabotage." Doreen Rawlins

The job of caregiving requires continual adjustments. Some of my bright ideas no longer work, as my husband declines. For having a sort of rigid personality, I've had to become *flexible*. These days, 'flexible' is my middle name. Probably ideas I've shared on earlier pages, don't work for me anymore. Perhaps they never worked for you in the first place. The symptoms of dementia disease have a common thread, but the ways they are displayed are all over the map.

Having taken care of my mother-in-law helped prepare me for taking care of her son in many ways. But don't think that because this or that worked in one case it will work in another. Don't be misled thinking you know what's coming next. There are many similarities, but no consistency, no pat answers.

As best as you can, take care of yourself honey, physically, mentally and spiritually. I've mentioned before there are good resources; the Internet, books and tapes on the subject. There are support groups available, home care and other forms of help. Don't become overwhelmed trying to find answers. Most likely the answers will change anyway.

In the earlier years, taking care of his mom there was very little help in any form. We put an ad in the local paper and interviewed several young women, seeking a nice (strong) gal to sit with Gramma for three hours, two mornings a week. It worked well in that case, at that time, giving us a break. It wouldn't work for me right now, but maybe a good solution for you.

Whatever your situation, mainly work on these three P's. Remain <u>positive</u>, change your <u>perspective</u> and <u>pray</u>.

"With God's help, we can do more than we think!" Amen

It's early morning – a purple socks day, the sun shines brightly, my coffee is hot. Why then, do I feel this niggling apprehension about facing a new day? Why does my responsibility seem heavier today? I'm walking on thin ice this morning – tired, weary and worn out. I'm in a rut, not practicing what I preach. I've been here before. Many times before. The feeling comes and goes. It's the feeling of *fear*.

As I go through the motions today, it will pass; this feeling of fear. I will pretend it's a headache that will go away. After all, I only need to make it until noon, right? One foot in front of the other, until noon. I seem to have neglected my "Pleasant Inns" along the way. Maybe it's time to "shake things up" as the TV ad says. Take off my purple stay-at-home socks and go to a movie! That's it. Today we'll go to a matinee.

There are so many unknowns to this disease, to the future. *What's gonna happen when or if. . . . . .* It's really no different than regular life. We don't know what will happen tomorrow – with or without sickness. Who can depend on tomorrow?

Some say there are only two feelings, *love* and *fear*. I must not allow fear to overcome! I must move into this day with confidence and trust in God.

Today, we shall enjoy an afternoon milkshake and go see "Wonder Woman". I'm beginning to feel better already.

"Don't be afraid of your fears. They're not there to scare you. They're there to let you know that something is worth it." Paul Coelho

Slogans can be helpful to the caregiver; not so much solutions as reminders. We've already talked about AA's mantra: "Let Go and Let God." I've written it down on post-it notes and strategically stuck them on the backside of cupboard doors.

Another catchphrase that is applicable to job of caregiver, is Nike's slogan "Just Do It". It helps to remember for those less than pleasant duties or the mundane responsibilities we must do over and over. Putting it off only makes things worse; Just Do It!

It's being disciplined to do what you must do, not only for and with the person you are caring for, but for yourself. You know, those nagging things we keep putting off. Recently I realized what was adding to my already stressful circumstances. I had put off a mammogram, needed a skin check with the dermatologist, and was way overdue for teeth cleaning. In addition, I had a basket of old mail to sort through and several phone calls to return. Nag, nag, nag!

Today I remember, the car needs gas – in fact, it's time for a full-service job. Plus, I need to make plans for a coming bridal shower, buy a gift and a card, figure out what to wear and what in the world I will do with my husband! I'm about to the point of caving-in, when I look in the mirror and notice my T-shirt. It's shouting- JUST DO IT!

I make a list and tackle the most dreaded job first. Just Do It. Crossing off one item at a time is such a relief. You will feel a weight lifted.

One more phrase that hangs on my wall, not on a post-it note but in a frame. It's embroidered. It's pretty. A gift from my best friend. It says:

"Do one thing every day that makes you happy."

When you've hit the wall and things aren't working with the one you're caring for, step back and take a deep breath. Maybe you need to change your approach. He is steadily declining. His world is getting narrower every day. But you keep doing the same thing; communicating the same old way. It's not working.

At the beginning of this project, my husband could get himself ready for bed. It was not always perfect and took a very long time. But once I had turned down the bed and set out his pajamas, he eventually got ready and climbed in. I would kiss him goodnight then and turn out the light.

These days, I must (without words) take him by the hand, lead him into the bedroom and undress him. In the beginning, he would argue and get angry when I tried to take off his shoes. By the end of the day, I'm not really in the mood for arguing. It's a waste of time and energy anyway. I began to make a game out of it, like you might with a child. From his bedroom chair, I will say, "Okay, stand up!" He will stand and I will whip his sweatpants down to the ankles. "Good job!", I say.

Then when I'm on my hands and knees, pulling off the pants, I get the shoes too. He doesn't have time to object. "Okay, stand up again!" He stands. "Atta boy!" This goes on until he's in his pajama bottoms, socks and the polo shirt he's worn all day. I give him choices, "Would you like to leave your socks on?" or "Would you like to sleep in your shirt?" Perhaps those choices give him a somewhat feeling of control.

Remember sweetie, he can't change. He's going to get worse. What worked yesterday, may be a disaster today. "Flexible" is now your middle name. Don't argue. Start over with whatever you're trying to accomplish. Make it a game. For your own sake, become an entertainer.

"If you only have one smile in you, give it to the people you love." Maya Angelou

When was the last time you bought yourself a lovely bunch of flowers? Or tried a new color lipstick? Or sautéed fresh mushrooms – just for you? When was the last time you did something to perk up the house? New pillows for the sofa perhaps. When was your last pedicure?

As a full time, round the clock caregiver, it would be easy to fall into a pit of despair. You're probably thinking, 'why bother? Who cares?' You don't invite people to come over anymore. Entertaining is a thing of the past. What difference does it make? Listen honey, you don't quit living, enjoying life because of the circumstances that came your way. You are a vital, important, beautiful person! It's okay to love yourself, to treat yourself now and then; to buy yourself something pretty.

Every day, I put my make-up on. It's a ritual that includes music. My mid-morning "Pleasant Inn." Every two weeks I get my nails done. (He comes with me; in case you're wondering.) Occasionally I purchase fresh flowers at the grocery store and arrange them in my favorite pewter pitcher. Last month, I ordered (good old Amazon) a new nightgown. My old ones were pathetic. The new gown is like sleeping in a cloud.

I'm not suggesting you must spend money to make yourself happy. In fact, you best save it! But don't let your circumstances turn you into a slothful mess. Life's little pleasures are within reach. Good books, music, hot coffee or mint tea. Do your job, taking care of him. But part of that job includes taking care of you! And one more thing, the secret to being truly beautiful – is to live your life with thankfulness.

"The miracle of gratitude is that it shifts your perception to such an extent that it changes the world you see." Dr. Robert Holden

During a time, when my husband was in deep pain with Sciatica, I purchased a lightweight transport chair. At first, I rented a regular heavy-duty wheelchair which Medicare covered, but getting it in and out of the car was a killer. I returned it after two days and purchased the lightweight chair. During a six-week period of his painful Sciatica, it was very much worth it. Since then the wheelchair has not been necessary, in fact – rejected! It's been in storage for nine months.

My dear man, used to be runner – five miles a day and ten or more on each birthday. He played tennis until he was eighty. He can still hit the ball, (I think it's called muscle memory) but has no clue about the score or where to stand. In fact, his playing buddies at the athletic club, had to graciously inform me when it was not working anymore. That he no longer "played well with others."

In recent months, his walking has slowed to a shuffle. If we walked any slower on our occasional evening strolls, we'd be going backwards. X-rays have shown heavy arthritis in his hips. I think it's time to put the wheelchair back in the car. In our town during summer months there are farmer's markets and street fairs galore. We haven't gone to anything like that in ages. Maybe it would work with the wheelchair. And if it does, in a few weeks, the County Fair. For both our sakes, we need to try new things or re-visit old.

"The only way to make sense out of change is to plunge into it, move with it and join the dance."
Alan W. Watts

It's been nineteen years ago that I sent myself a card. We had moved from the city to our vacation cabin in Central Oregon, bringing my husband's mom with us. She had been widowed for three years and failing with dementia. That was in July of 1998. The card came that fall, addressed to me — *from* me. I'm viewing it now as I do periodically.

It's a Mary Engelbreit card. The image is of a girl in a painter's smock and French beret, painting a lovely scene on the walls of her apartment; the only window looking out on a brick building. It's an outdoor scene she's painting; blue skies, white clouds, green rolling hills and flowers galore; the main feature an apple tree, loaded with apples.

The caption below reads, "If you don't like something change it. If you can't change it, change the way you think about it!" — The first quote in this journal.

In the disease of dementia, there's nothing we can change. We've discovered a few helpful solutions and some better ways of responding, but the sad truth, dementia can't be fixed. In my private moments, I wonder why it happens. Why did it happen to him? Why did it happen to me? Why does it have to happen to anyone?

God works in mysterious ways! In this caregiving journey, me caring for him, God is doing his redeeming work in me. In the daily struggles of caregiving, I am continually growing in dependence on Him, realizing my need of Him. I am being transformed into a new and different person. I am changing the way I think about it; painting the hopeless walls of dementia with blue skies and flowers galore.

"Don't copy the behavior and customs of this world but be a new and different person with a fresh newness in all you do and think." Romans *12:2**

---

* TLB

Helps and Resources:

Charmin Strong – Single-ply toilet paper
Commercial type plunger
Wet Ones
Spot Shot – carpet stain remover
Clorox Bathroom Cleaner with Bleach
Clorox Disinfectant Wipes
Charcoal Room Deodorizer
Fabreeze Air Freshener
Vinegar
Baking Soda

Depends for Men
Petey's Washable Padded Briefs for Men
Protective Mattress Pads

Melatonin* 5mg – help for sleep
Night-Lights

The Thirty-Six Hour Day by Nancy L. Mace and Peter V. Rabins
Learning to Speak Alzheimer's by Joanne Koenig Coste
Creating Moments of Joy by Jolene Brackey

Alzheimer's Cargiver's Guide and Sourcebook by Howard Gruetzner

Living with Alzheimer's – Chicken Soup for the Soul – Alzheimer's Assn.

It's All In Your Approach (DVD) by Teepa Snow

*Melatonin can cause diarrhea in some cases.

PS –

Since beginning this project, things have changed in many ways. My husband has more extreme mood changes. His eating problem (Dysphagia) has worsened. He's not entirely there yet but headed toward incontinence with more frequent accidents. It works best to keep our social encounters to even more a minimum. He sleeps a lot; tired much of the time.

When I re-read what I've written over the past 52 weeks, it seems but a feeble attempt to communicate the indescribable. Daily there are exchanges between us that, short of a video would be impossible to depict. I feel my efforts are terribly inadequate of the intention for this book.

In my "you go girl!" attitude, I don't always feel like that. I must pick myself up by the bootstraps a dozen times a day – some days more than others. It's usually the result of my not eating right, not getting sleep – in short, not taking care of myself.

Also, feeling obligated to other people can side-track me from my job, causing frustration.

The good news is, that in my own deficiency, my reliance has grown more and more on the Lord. He gives me *strength* and *hope* as I'm learning to trust Him, one half day at a time. Remember dear one, you are not alone.

"LORD, help me to remember that nothing is going to happen to me today that YOU AND I can't handle TOGETHER." Anonymous

Epilogue

Since writing those fifty-two pages, I've had to reluctantly move my husband to a memory care facility. His dementia continues to spiral downward. Looking back, the things I've written are still relevant and hopefully beneficial to you dedicated caregivers. It's just that now, considering new challenges in a new environment with new people, so much more needs to be said. The move has been an emotional rollercoaster for both of us, however in different ways. He is in another world, in more ways than one. The adjustment for him has been difficult logistically; not knowing where the bathroom is, not knowing where his apartment is and not knowing the people; other residents and staff. A mix of caregivers on different shifts and on different days take care of him. It would be confusing to anyone.

Often friends and family think, now that he's being cared for in a facility, I have the freedom to do whatever I please, go wherever I wish. There is a benefit to doing things I haven't been able to do for a long time. It's like getting out of jail —

after so many years of being tied down. I don't take it for granted! But there is no way I can cut the ties fully. It's a struggle for me to let go and let others care for him. After searching out the best possible place for him, none really measures up to my standards. I'm determined to keep the staff accountable in his care.

When he moved from home into memory care, he hadn't been on medication of any kind. Over the first three months, our doctor had prescribed small doses of meds to help him sleep and balance his temperament, which has been extreme - from extra sweet to displays of aggressive behavior. The medication thing has been a very long process; each change requires following certain time-consuming protocol. Then, the "wait and see" if anything changes. My advice is to start the medication process *before* making a move to memory care.

Care facilities all seem to have a waiting list. Even if you feel a move may be a way off, I suggest visiting all the possibilities in your area, taking the tour and getting a packet of information. If possible, take a family member with you. Two heads are better than one. Be informed about your options for when and if the time comes. One of the higher-end memory care places in our city, has a waitlist of six to nine months. Some facilities are obviously better than others, but my conclusion is there is no perfect place.

In the beginning of our transition, I visited my husband everyday always finding things to complain about regarding his care, his room, his laundry etc. The computerized, comprehensive schedule I was given, was hardly ever followed. On his scheduled shower days, for example, I would arrive in the afternoon to find him in yesterday's soiled clothing, maybe with his pj's on top and toothpaste plastered in his hair! The laundry basket was often over-flowing, and the floor of his room sticky with urine. Besides the fact that he's my husband and I want the very best for him, the cost of his care is flabbergasting! Because he was so "lost" all the time, his care requirements elevated the first few weeks to the highest level and highest cost.

Several things have helped the situation. Mainly, I have changed my attitude from always complaining to the staff to becoming friends with them. Also, I've made a point of getting to know the other residents – there are twenty-four in all - in my husband's community. (A good quote to inject here would be "Bloom where you are planted.") I've lowered my standards and picked up where the staff has fallen short, taking some laundry home, cleaning up his room at times, changing sheets as necessary and tending to my husband as needed. Mostly, I've learned to let go, and make the best of the situation. I spend most afternoons there with him or take him for a drive. Once a week I take one whole day for myself.

Most recently, I've linked him up with a new doctor, one that makes house calls to the facility and is highly qualified in the area of dementia. He has started a new medication and as before, it takes two or three weeks to really see the results. It seems to be working better – he is less agitated and it's so nice to have the doctor come to him.

When I visit, I carry a tote bag with necessities, other than what is kept in his closet. Everything from nail clippers and other grooming items to Wet Swifters in a plastic bag. These I use for sticky spots on the floor to mop up with my foot directing the Swifter pad, instead of the mop handle. I have made his room homey with pictures and quilts, but we family members are encouraged not to bring anything of value. So far, his glasses, his favorite Billy Graham book, one slipper and a variety of other things are missing. On the other hand, all kinds of stuff from other apartments, show up in his room! Often, he's dressed in another resident's clothing when I arrive. It's irritating but not life-threatening. Que Sera Sera.

There are certainly wonderful administrative folks, med-techs and caregivers that do a less than desirable job every day. As I've come to know them, I have more appreciation for each one. Often someone is caring for *their* children, feeding and changing diapers – while many of these staff people are doing the same for old folks, because they need to pay their bills just like the rest of us. Most, truly love the work of nurturing, recognizing most memory care residents can't communicate or follow directions and, in some cases must even be fed. Much of the day for caregivers in memory care communities, is spent "re-directing" the individual and cleaning up after them – repeatedly.

For me, being an active assistant for at least a few hours each day, is a win-win deal. I am spending time with my husband, making sure his needs are met, building a relationship with a variety of caregivers as well as housekeepers and staying on top of the mundane things such as hygiene and laundry. Most days I take him out for a drive in the country with milkshakes and music;

another help for all involved. He's content, I'm content and it's a bit of a break for the staff.

The greatest blessing is getting to know others in the memory care neighborhood. My husband enjoys his meals at a table with the same three gentlemen daily; each one in their own way, very funny – at least to me. Every evening at dinner I pull up a chair and sit with "my boys". Oh my; I could write a book about our conversations! The stories are endless from their days of rodeo, drag racing, playing professional football – "that's when the big bucks came rolling in!" And of course, one went to school with Elvis and another tells jokes that nobody gets and says, "top that one!" Then there's poor old Robert – so sweet, just nodding in agreement with everyone's story until he nods off, forehead in applesauce. My husband rarely joins in our conversations, being consumed with the whole eating process. It takes him much longer to clean his plate as he's so meticulous these days. Because of his swallowing issue all his meals come finely chopped. I dread when rice is part of the meal. It takes forever when a guy eats one grain of rice at a time!

I've had to resort to a bit of scheming when I'm ready to leave for the evening. If I were to tell him I was leaving, or that it was time to go, or that I was going home, it wouldn't work at all - in his case anyway. He would jump up – even in the middle of his unfinished rice – and insist on going with me. It may sound harsh, but the best thing is just to sneak out. Typically, when he's occupied with dessert, I can make my escape. They say he looks for me sometimes, but usually just goes with the flow – as if I hadn't been there at all. Every evening though, on my way out the back door, I stop at his room and leave a baggie of his favorite Golden Oreos under the pillow. Driving home, I pray for him – that he will sleep well and be content; and that the bag of cookies will make him smile.

If you are caring for someone with Alzheimer Disease, here's my counsel. Take action now to get your legal ducks in a row, by seeking advice from an elder law attorney. In addition to preparation of legal documents, an updated Will, Power of Attorney and Advanced Directive, it's possible your parent, or spouse may qualify for Medicaid. Take a tour of memory care facilities and gather information for the future. And mostly, take care of you, dear heart and God bless you in the journey.

I would love to hear from you with questions or comments on my blog. www.doreenrawlins.com.

Made in United States
Orlando, FL
21 April 2022

17061176R00131